Learn to Read with Zeb

Volume 1

Carol Zerboni

Learn to Read with Zeb, Volume 1
Copyright 2017, 2021 by Carol Zerboni, Zeb Books, LLC

Layout by www.formatting4U.com

www.ZebBooks.com

Print ISBN: 978-1-942666-35-6
Digital ISBN: 978-1-942666-36-3

Table of Contents

Zeb Books

"Zeb"

Draw a picture about this Zeb Book!

Zeb is a dog.

Zeb is a pup.

Deb is his Mom.

Jed is his Dad.

Run Zeb, run!

Get the hat, Zeb.

Zeb ran to the hat.

The hat is on top of Zeb.

Zeb has a pal. Max
is the pal of Zeb.

Max and Zeb run. It is a lot of fun to run.

Zeb Books

"Ten"

Draw a
picture about
this Zeb Book!

Ten cats.

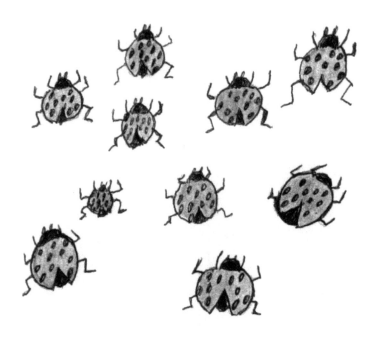

Ten bugs sit.

Deb the dog is ten.

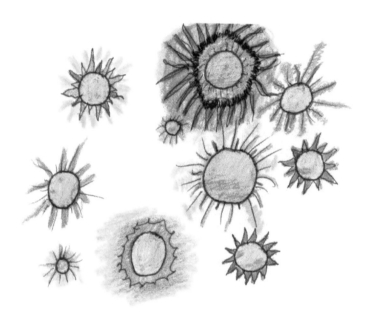

Ten hot suns.

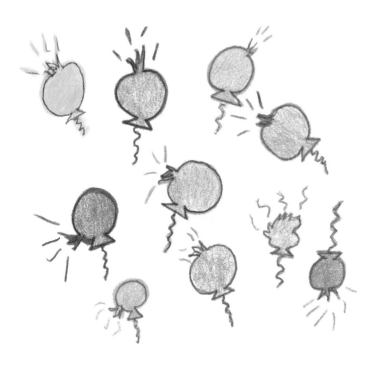

Ten big pops!

Pam the pig is ten.

Bob has on ten wigs.

Ten bats nap.

The mop has a ten
on it.

The end of ten.

Zeb Books

"Sid"

Draw a
picture about
this Zeb Book!

Sid is a bug.

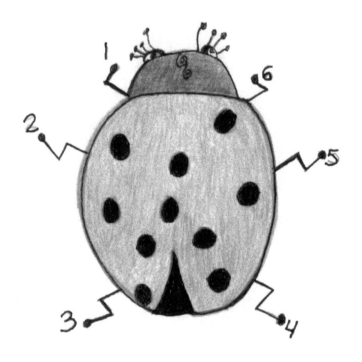

Sid has six legs.

Sid can sit.

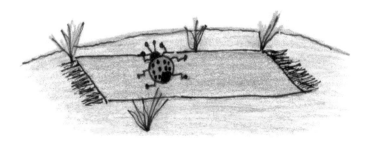

Sid can sit on a rug.

Sid got up on the top
of a mop.

Sid is on the hat.

Sid has ten dots.

Sid hid on the wig.

Sid has a big box. It has a bed in it.

Sid has fun in the sun. Big fun!

Zeb Books

"The Mop"

Draw a
picture about
this Zeb Book!

The mop is big.

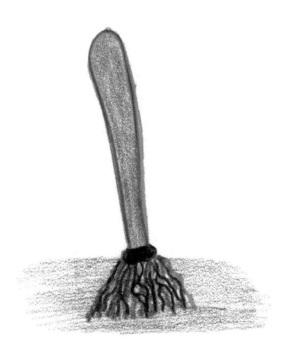

The mop is red.

The mop is big and red.

The mop is hot and wet.

Bob can get up on top
of the big, red mop.

Bob can hop on top of the big, red mop.

The mop is on top of Bob. The mop is his wig!

Bob sat on a mat. Bob set the mop on the mat. The big, red mop is on the mat and it is wet.

Bob got the mop and set it in the sun! It is hot in the sun. The mop is not wet. Bob is hot. Bob got the mop and ran.

The big, red mop is fun! Bob had fun! The big, red mop is fun, big fun!

Zeb Books

"Bob the Cat"

Draw a
picture about
this Zeb Book!

Zeb has a fun pal.

His pal is Bob.

Bob is a cat.

Bob can jig.

Bob is in a wig.

Bob is up on a big mop.

Bob is on top of a pig.

Bob can sit.
Sit cat, sit.

Bob is up.
Go Bob, go.

Zeb, Bob and the pigs
are pals.

Zeb Books

"Pam the Pig"

Draw a picture about this Zeb Book!

Pam is a pig.

Pat sits in the sun.

Pam has fun in the
mud. Pam can dig.

Pip is a pal of Pam.
Pip is a big pig.

Pip and Pam dig in the mud.

It is a lot of fun to dig in the mud.

Big fun!

Pam dug up
a pan of mud.

Pam set the pan of mud on the rug. Pam had a nap on the rug.

Pam has a nap. Pip can get the pan of mud. No, Pip! No!

Pam had to get a wet rag. Pam got the mud off Pip.

Pip and his gal pal, Pam, had fun.

Zeb Books

"Ben the Bat"

Draw a
picture about
this Zeb Book!

Ben is a big bat.

Ben has a sis.
The sis is Liz.

Ben is ten.
Liz is six.

Ben and Liz can go up
to a big map. The map
has an "X" on it.

Ben tells Liz, "Let us go to the 'X' on the map."

Ben and Liz get to
the "X" on the map.
The "X" is on a big,
red cup.

The big, red cup has gum in it. Gum is not for a bat.

Ben and Liz can not get bugs. A ham is on the rug. Ham is not for bats.

Ben and Liz sit on a log. Bugs are on the log.

Yum! Yum! It is fun to
get the bugs.

Oh, no! The sun is up. The sun is not for bats.

Ben and Liz go to bed. It is a fun, bat bed.

Zeb Books

"The Hat"

Draw a
picture about
this Zeb Book!

The hat is big. It can fit Deb.

Deb can go to the
vet. The vet is a man.
The hat is on Deb.

Deb has a nap. A hen
has a bib. The hen
can put on the hat.
The hen ran.

The hat is big on the hen. The hat is for a dog, not a hen.

The hat is on the rug.
Zeb can get the hat.
Zeb can run to the hat.

Zeb can put Max in
the hat. Jed, the dad
of Zeb, tells the
pups, "No!"

Jed can get the hat
to Deb. It is up on
top of Deb. The hat
is for Deb.

Deb can get the hat
to Liz, the bat, but it
is big. It did not fit.

Pam can put on the hat. It is not big on a pig.

Deb can let Bob put the hat up on top of his big, red mop.

Deb has on a big, red
wig. Deb can get the
hat and put it on top
of the wig.

Deb got the hat and sat on the rug. A hat is big fun.

Zeb Books

"The Rug"

Draw a picture about this Zeb Book!

The rug is big. Zeb, the pup, met his bud, Max, on the rug. Zeb and Max sit on the rug and nap.

Deb and Jed sat on
the rug. Deb fed Jed
ham and jam in a mug
on the rug. Deb and
Jed nap on the rug.

Bob can sit on the rug in the sun. It is hot in the sun. It is hot on the rug. Bob can not nap. Bob got his rod and ran.

Pam and Pip sit in the sun on the rug. Pam and Pip hug the rug and get a tan. It is hot in the sun. It was fun to tan.

Ben and Liz sit on the
rug. A bug is on the
rug. Ben can get the
bug. Yum! Liz can get
the bug on the rug.
Yum! Ben and Liz can
nap on the rug.

The hat is on the rug.
Oh, no! The rug is wet.
It is bad to get a rug
wet. It is wet and mud
got on the rug. The
hat has mud on it.

Pam got a big tub. It is
a big job to get the mud
off the rug and hat.
Pam has a wet rag. Pam
can rub the mud off.
Pam can fan the rug.
The sun is up and the
rug is not wet.

The rug is in the sun.
It is not wet. The man
in the cap has a bag.
The man has a pet hen
in the bag. The man and
his hen sit on the rug.

The hen is not in the bag. The hen can sit on the leg of the man. The hen and the man sit on the rug.

The pals met at the rug. The rug is big, but the pals can not fit on it. Oh, no!

A jet can get the rug to go up. Up! Up! The rug can go up on top of a big, tin bus!

The rug is up on top
of the big, red bus.
The bus will go get
the pals.

Zeb Books

"The Big Red Bus"

Draw a picture about this Zeb Book!

The bus is big. The bus is red. It is a big, red bus.

Pam and Pip can get on the big, red bus. It is fun to go on the big, red bus.

Zeb and Max ran to get on the big, red bus. Deb and Jed ran to get on the big, red bus.

Deb has on the hat.
The hat is on top of
Deb. Deb and the hat
are on the bus.

The bus can stop. Bob can get on the bus. A cat, a hat, dogs and pigs are on the big, red bus.

The bus will stop for Ben and his sis, Liz. The bats get on the bus.

Oh, no! The rug is up on top of the big, red bus. Bob will go get the rug off the bus.

The big, red bus can fit a lot of pals in it. A rug, a hat, a cat, bats, dogs and pigs are on the big, red bus.

The big, red bus can go up, up, up! It is fun to go up on the big, red bus.

The big, red bus will stop. The pals got on the big rug to nap.

Oh, no! The sun is up. The sun is not for bats. Ben and Liz will go to bed. The bus will stop.

The pals got off the bus. The pals had fun on the big, red bus. Big fun!

Letters and Sounds

Zeb Books

apple

Aa

bat

Bb

cat

dog

Dd

egg

Ee

fish

goat

Gg

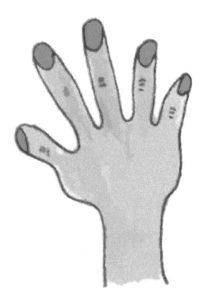

hand

igloo

Ii

jet

kite

Kk

lollipop

moon

nest

octopus

pig

queen

rabbit

sun

Ss

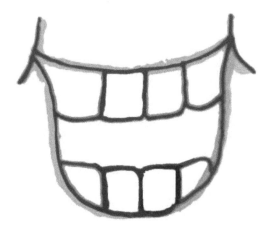

teeth

umbrella   Uu

valentine

wagon

x-ray

yo-yo

zebra

Zz

Peek

Aa		apple	(ah)
Bb		bat	(buh)
Cc		cat	(cuh)
Dd		dog	(duh)
Ee		egg	(eh)
Ff		fish	(fuh)
Gg		goat	(guh)

Peek

Hh		hand	(huh)
Ii		igloo	(ih)
Jj		jet	(juh)
Kk		kite	(kuh)
Ll		lollipop	(luh)
Mm		moon	(muh)
Nn		nest	(nuh)

Peek

Oo		octopus	(ahh)
Pp		pig	(puh)
Qq		queen	(quh)
Rr		rabbit	(ruh)
Ss		sun	(suh)
Tt		teeth	(tuh)
Uu		umbrella	(uh)

Peek

		valentine	(vuh)
		wagon	(wuh)
		x-ray	(ex)
		yo-yo	(yuh)
		zebra	(zuh)

Blending Sounds to Make Words

Zeb Books

Sound it out:

a

is

an

on

it

up

in

as

at

am

Sound it out:

cat

dog

pig

rat

mop

ten

bug

Sound it out:

vet

kit

has

fan

get

nut

leg

yet

Sound it out:

sun

wig

fun

cut

big

hot

log

zip

rod

cab

Rhyming Words

Zeb Books

bad	bag	can
dad	rag	fan
had	tag	man
mad	wag	pan
pad		ran
sad		tan
		van

cap	bat
lap	cat
map	hat
nap	mat
rap	pat
tap	rat
	sat
	vat

beg	den	bet
keg	hen	get
leg	men	met
peg	pen	net
	ten	pet
		vet

bin	bib	dip
kin	fib	hip
fin	nib	lip
pin		nip
tin		rip
win		sip
		tip

bop	cot
cop	dot
hop	got
mop	hot
pop	lot
top	not
	pot
	rot
	tot

bun	bum	but
fun	gum	cut
nun	hum	hut
pun	sum	nut
run		rut
sun		

About the Author

The Zeb Books are written and illustrated by Carol Zerboni. Carol is a lifetime member of the American Montessori Society & has owned her own Montessori Preschool and Kindergarten for 40 years. Carol has taught reading to children ages 3-7 for 49 years using the Montessori approach with phonics.

Printed in the USA
CPSIA information can be obtained
at www.ICGtesting.com
LVHW070728311023
762621LV00050BA/1426